75 DAY

challenge

 follow a diet of your choice

 do two 45 minute workouts per day (one must be outside)

 zero alcohol, no cheat meals

 post a progress picture daily

 drink 1-gallon of water daily

 read 10 pages in a book daily

for 75 days straight or, start over again!

SPS Press

notes:

NOW ♠

MENTAL TOUGHNESS STARTS NOW

To provide a review on www.Amazon.com
1. click the link on your orders button
2. follow to this book
3. leave an honest review of your experience
Thanks in advance! Everyone will benefit!

CONFIDENCE
SELF-ESTEEM
SELF-WORTH
SELF-BELIEF
FORTITUDE
GRITTINESS

use this journal to finish the program

name: ....

notes:

75 DAY PLAN

art Date .... Start Weight ....

d Date .... Goal Weight ....

1 ○ ○ ○ ○ ○ ○ ○ ○ ○ ○

○ ○ ○ ○ ○ ○ ○ ○ ○ ○

○ ○ ○ ○ ○ ○ ○ ○ ○ ○

○ ○ ○ ○ ○ ○ ○ ○ ○ ○

○ ○ ○ ○ ○ ○ ○ ○ ○ ○

○ ○ ○ ○ ○ ○ ○ ○ ○ ○

○ ○ (75)

*track your progress as
you complete your tasks*

notes:

NOW

Date: dd / mm / yyyy   Day: /   NOW ♠

Diet

Breakfast   3 eggs, 4 bacon, toast
almonds

Lunch avocado salad with 1000 islands dressing
protein shake with blueberries

Dinner   beef and bean chili
3 carrots

Water
8-sixteen oz pints of water

Post Picture

Exercise

6am, 20 mins cardio

3 sets, 20 squats

4 sets, 80lb calf raise

2 sets, 100lb deadlift

stretch

Exercise

8pm, 20 mins cardio

3 sets, 20lb curls

3 sets, 30lb flys
4 sets, 20lb trys

10 mins core

Book Atomic Habits   Pages   1-75

notes:

NOW ♠

Date: _____   Day: _____   NOW ♠

Diet

....
Breakfast

....
Lunch

....
Dinner

....
Water ⊔ ⊔ ⊔ ⊔ ⊔ ⊔ ⊔ ⊔
....

Post Picture ☐

Exercise	Exercise

Book ....   Pages ....

notes:

Date: Day:

NOW ♠

Diet

Breakfast

Lunch

Dinner

Water ▽▽▽▽▽▽▽▽

Post Picture ☐

Exercise	Exercise

Book .... Pages ....

notes:

NOW

Date: Day:

Diet

Breakfast

Lunch

Dinner

Water

Post Picture ☐

Exercise	Exercise

Book .... Pages ....

notes:

Date: Day: NOW ♠

Diet

Breakfast

Lunch

Dinner

Water

Post Picture ☐

Exercise	Exercise

Book .... Pages ....

notes:

NOW

Date: Day: NOW

Diet

Breakfast

Lunch

Dinner

Water 🥤🥤🥤🥤🥤🥤🥤🥤

Post Picture ☐

Exercise	Exercise

Book .... Pages ....

notes:

NOW

Date: Day: NOW ♠

Diet

Breakfast

Lunch

Dinner

Water

Post Picture ☐

Exercise	Exercise

Book ....   Pages ....

notes:

NOW

Date: _____   Day: _____   NOW ♠

Diet

Breakfast

Lunch

Dinner

Water ⊔ ⊔ ⊔ ⊔ ⊔ ⊔ ⊔ ⊔

Post Picture ☐

Exercise	Exercise

Book .... Pages ....

notes:

Date: Day: NOW ♠

Diet

Breakfast

Lunch

Dinner

Water

Post Picture ☐

Exercise	Exercise

Book .... Pages ....

notes:

Date: Day: NOW ♠

Diet

Breakfast

Lunch

Dinner

Water

Post Picture ☐

Exercise	Exercise

Book .... Pages ....

notes:

Date: Day: **NOW** ♠

Diet

Breakfast

Lunch

Dinner

Water ⊔ ⊔ ⊔ ⊔ ⊔ ⊔ ⊔ ⊔

Post Picture ☐

Exercise	Exercise

Book .... Pages ....

notes:

NOW

Date: _____ Day: _____ NOW ♠

Diet

Breakfast

....

Lunch

....

Dinner

....

Water 🥛🥛🥛🥛🥛🥛🥛🥛

Post Picture ☐

Exercise	Exercise

Book .... Pages ....

notes:

NOW ♠

Date: _____ Day: _____

Diet

Breakfast

Lunch

Dinner

Water ⊔ ⊔ ⊔ ⊔ ⊔ ⊔ ⊔ ⊔

Post Picture ☐

Exercise	Exercise

Book .... Pages ....

notes:

Date: Day: **NOW** ♠

Diet

Breakfast

Lunch

Dinner

Water ▽▽▽▽▽▽▽▽

Post Picture ☐

Exercise	Exercise

Book .... Pages ....

notes:

NOW ♠

Date: Day: NOW ♠

Diet

Breakfast

Lunch

Dinner

Water ⊔ ⊔ ⊔ ⊔ ⊔ ⊔ ⊔ ⊔

Post Picture ☐

Exercise	Exercise

Book .... Pages ....

notes:

NOW

Date: Day: NOW ♠

Diet

Breakfast

Lunch

Dinner

Water 🥛🥛🥛🥛🥛🥛🥛🥛

Post Picture ☐

Exercise	Exercise

Book .... Pages ....

notes:

NOW

Date: Day: NOW ♠

Diet

Breakfast

Lunch

Dinner

Water 🥛🥛🥛🥛🥛🥛🥛🥛

Post Picture ☐

Exercise	Exercise

Book .... Pages ....

notes:

Date: Day: NOW ♠

Diet

Breakfast

Lunch

Dinner

Water ⊔⊔⊔⊔⊔⊔⊔⊔

Post Picture ☐

Exercise	Exercise

Book .... Pages ....

notes:

NOW

Date: Day: **NOW**

Diet

Breakfast

Lunch

Dinner

Water 🥤🥤🥤🥤🥤🥤🥤🥤

Post Picture ☐

Exercise	Exercise

Book   Pages

notes:

NOW

Date: Day: **NOW** ♠

Diet

Breakfast

Lunch

Dinner

Water ▽ ▽ ▽ ▽ ▽ ▽ ▽ ▽

Post Picture ☐

Exercise	Exercise

Book .... Pages ....

notes:

NOW

Date: Day: NOW ♠

Diet

Breakfast

Lunch

Dinner

Water

Post Picture ☐

Exercise	Exercise

Book   Pages

notes:

NOW ♠

Date: Day: NOW ♠

Diet

Breakfast

Lunch

Dinner

Water

Post Picture ☐

Exercise	Exercise

Book .... Pages ....

notes:

NOW

Date: Day: NOW ♠

Diet

Breakfast

Lunch

Dinner

Water ⊔ ⊔ ⊔ ⊔ ⊔ ⊔ ⊔ ⊔

Post Picture ☐

Exercise   Exercise

Book   Pages

notes:

NOW

Date: Day: **NOW** ♠

Diet

Breakfast

Lunch

Dinner

Water 🥛🥛🥛🥛🥛🥛🥛🥛

Post Picture ☐

Exercise	Exercise

Book .... Pages ....

notes:

NOW

Date: Day: NOW ♠

Diet

Breakfast

Lunch

Dinner

Water

Post Picture ☐

Exercise	Exercise

Book   Pages

notes:

NOW

Date: Day:

NOW ♠

Diet

Breakfast

Lunch

Dinner

Water ⊔⊔⊔⊔⊔⊔⊔⊔

Post Picture ☐

Exercise	Exercise

Book   Pages

notes:

Date: Day: NOW ♠

Diet

Breakfast

Lunch

Dinner

Water ⊔⊔⊔⊔⊔⊔⊔⊔

Post Picture ☐

Exercise	Exercise

Book .... Pages ....

notes:

NOW

Date: Day: NOW ♠

Diet

Breakfast

Lunch

Dinner

Water 🥛🥛🥛🥛🥛🥛🥛🥛

Post Picture ☐

Exercise	Exercise

Book Pages

notes:

NOW ♠

Date: Day: NOW

Diet

Breakfast

Lunch

Dinner

Water ⊔⊔⊔⊔⊔⊔⊔⊔

Post Picture ☐

Exercise	Exercise

Book .... Pages ....

notes:

NOW ♠

Date: Day: **NOW** ♠

Diet

Breakfast

Lunch

Dinner

Water 🥛🥛🥛🥛🥛🥛🥛🥛

Post Picture ☐

Exercise	Exercise

Book   Pages

notes:

NOW ♠

Date: Day: NOW ♠

Diet

Breakfast

Lunch

Dinner

Water

Post Picture ☐

Exercise	Exercise

Book .... Pages ....

notes:

Date: Day: **NOW**

Diet

Breakfast

Lunch

Dinner

Water

Post Picture ☐

Exercise	Exercise

Book .... Pages ....

notes:

NOW ♠

Date: Day: **NOW** ♠

Diet

Breakfast

Lunch

Dinner

Water 🥛🥛🥛🥛🥛🥛🥛🥛

Post Picture ☐

Exercise	Exercise

Book .... Pages ....

notes:

NOW ♠

Date: Day: NOW ♠

Diet

Breakfast
....

Lunch
....

Dinner
....

Water 🥛🥛🥛🥛🥛🥛🥛🥛

Post Picture ☐

Exercise	Exercise

Book .... Pages ....

notes:

NOW ♠

Date: Day: **NOW** ♠

Diet

Breakfast

Lunch

Dinner

Water

Post Picture ☐

Exercise	Exercise

Book   Pages

notes:

Date: Day: NOW ♠

Diet
Breakfast

Lunch

Dinner

Water 🥤🥤🥤🥤🥤🥤🥤🥤

Post Picture ☐

Exercise	Exercise

Book .... Pages ....

notes:

NOW ♠

Date: Day: **NOW** ♠

Diet

Breakfast

Lunch

Dinner

Water ⊔⊔⊔⊔⊔⊔⊔⊔

Post Picture ☐

Exercise	Exercise

Book .... Pages ....

notes:

NOW

Date: Day: **NOW** ♠

Diet

Breakfast

Lunch

Dinner

Water ⊔ ⊔ ⊔ ⊔ ⊔ ⊔ ⊔ ⊔

Post Picture ☐

Exercise	Exercise

Book .... Pages ....

notes:

Date: Day: **NOW** ♠

Diet

Breakfast

Lunch

Dinner

Water

Post Picture ☐

Exercise	Exercise

Book   Pages

notes:

NOW ♠

Date: _____   Day: _____   NOW ♠

Diet

Breakfast
....

Lunch
....

Dinner
....

Water ⊔⊔⊔⊔⊔⊔⊔⊔

Post Picture ☐

Exercise	Exercise

Book ....   Pages ....

notes:

NOW

Date: Day: **NOW** ♠

Diet

Breakfast

Lunch

Dinner

Water ⊔ ⊔ ⊔ ⊔ ⊔ ⊔ ⊔ ⊔

Post Picture ☐

Exercise	Exercise

Book .... Pages ....

notes:

NOW

Date: Day: NOW ♠

Diet

Breakfast

Lunch

Dinner

Water ⊔⊔⊔⊔⊔⊔⊔⊔

Post Picture ☐

Exercise	Exercise

Book ....   Pages ....

notes:

NOW ♠

Date: Day: **NOW** ♠

Diet

Breakfast

Lunch

Dinner

Water ⊔⊔⊔⊔⊔⊔⊔⊔

Post Picture ☐

Exercise	Exercise

Book Pages

notes:

NOW

Date: Day: NOW

Diet

Breakfast

Lunch

Dinner

Water

Post Picture ☐

Exercise	Exercise

Book   Pages

notes:

NOW

Date: Day: **NOW** ♠

Diet

Breakfast

Lunch

Dinner

Water 🥤🥤🥤🥤🥤🥤🥤🥤

Post Picture ☐

Exercise	Exercise

Book ....   Pages ....

notes:

NOW ♠

Date: Day:

NOW ♠

Diet

Breakfast

Lunch

Dinner

Water ▽▽▽▽▽▽▽▽

Post Picture ☐

Exercise	Exercise

Book

Pages

notes:

NOW ♠

Date: Day:

NOW ♠

Diet

Breakfast

Lunch

Dinner

Water ⊔ ⊔ ⊔ ⊔ ⊔ ⊔ ⊔ ⊔

Post Picture ☐

Exercise	Exercise

Book Pages

notes:

Date: Day:

NOW ♠

Diet

Breakfast

Lunch

Dinner

Water ▽▽▽▽▽▽▽▽

Post Picture ☐

Exercise	Exercise

Book Pages

notes:

Date: Day: NOW ♠

Diet

Breakfast

Lunch

Dinner

Water ▽▽▽▽▽▽▽▽

Post Picture ☐

Exercise	Exercise

Book ....   Pages ....

notes:

NOW ♠

Date: Day: **NOW** ♠

Diet

Breakfast

Lunch

Dinner

Water ⌴⌴⌴⌴⌴⌴⌴⌴

Post Picture ☐

Exercise   ## Exercise

Book   Pages

notes:

NOW ♠

Date: Day: NOW

Diet

Breakfast

Lunch

Dinner

Water

Post Picture ☐

Exercise	Exercise

Book Pages

notes:

NOW

Date: _____ Day: _____ NOW ♠

Diet

....

Breakfast

....

Lunch

....

Dinner

....

Water 🥛🥛🥛🥛🥛🥛🥛🥛

....

Post Picture ☐

Exercise	Exercise

Book .... Pages ....

notes:

NOW

Date: Day: NOW

Diet

Breakfast

Lunch

Dinner

Water

Post Picture ☐

Exercise	Exercise

Book   Pages

notes:

NOW

Date: Day:

NOW ♠

Diet

Breakfast

Lunch

Dinner

Water ⊔⊔⊔⊔⊔⊔⊔⊔

Post Picture ☐

Exercise	Exercise

Book .... Pages ....

notes:

NOW

Date: Day: NOW

Diet

Breakfast

Lunch

Dinner

Water

Post Picture ☐

Exercise	Exercise

Book .... Pages ....

notes:

NOW ♠

Date: Day: NOW ♠

Diet

Breakfast

Lunch

Dinner

Water ⊔⊔⊔⊔⊔⊔⊔⊔

Post Picture ☐

Exercise	Exercise

Book .... Pages ....

notes:

NOW ♠

Date: _____   Day: _____   NOW ♠

Diet
Breakfast ....

Lunch ....

Dinner ....

Water 🥤🥤🥤🥤🥤🥤🥤🥤

Post Picture ☐

Exercise	Exercise

Book ....   Pages ....

notes:

NOW ♠

Date: Day: NOW ♠

Diet

Breakfast

Lunch

Dinner

Water ⊔⊔⊔⊔⊔⊔⊔⊔

Post Picture ☐

Exercise	Exercise

Book .... Pages ....

notes:

NOW ♠

Date: Day: NOW ♠

Diet

Breakfast

Lunch

Dinner

Water ⊔⊔⊔⊔⊔⊔⊔⊔

Post Picture ☐

Exercise	Exercise

Book .... Pages ....

notes:

NOW

Date: Day: NOW

Diet

Breakfast

Lunch

Dinner

Water ⊔⊔⊔⊔⊔⊔⊔⊔

Post Picture ☐

Exercise	Exercise

Book .... Pages ....

notes:

Date: Day: **NOW** ♠

Diet

Breakfast

Lunch

Dinner

Water ⊔⊔⊔⊔⊔⊔⊔⊔

Post Picture ☐

Exercise	Exercise

Book .... Pages ....

notes:

Date: Day: NOW

Diet

Breakfast

Lunch

Dinner

Water 🥤🥤🥤🥤🥤🥤🥤🥤

Post Picture ☐

Exercise   # Exercise

Book   Pages

notes:

NOW

Date: Day:

NOW

Diet

Breakfast

Lunch

Dinner

Water 〜〜 〜〜 〜〜 〜〜 〜〜 〜〜 〜〜 〜〜

Post Picture ☐

Exercise	Exercise

Book .... Pages ....

notes:

NOW

Date: Day:

Diet

Breakfast

Lunch

Dinner

Water ⊔⊔⊔⊔⊔⊔⊔⊔

Post Picture ☐

Exercise	Exercise

Book .... Pages ....

notes:

NOW ♠

Date: Day: **NOW** ♠

Diet

Breakfast

Lunch

Dinner

Water   ▽▽▽▽▽▽▽▽

Post Picture ☐

Exercise	Exercise

Book .... Pages ....

notes:

NOW

Date: Day: NOW ♠

Diet

Breakfast

Lunch

Dinner

Water

Post Picture ☐

Exercise	Exercise

Book   Pages

notes:

NOW

Date: Day: **NOW** ♠

Diet

Breakfast

Lunch

Dinner

Water 🥤🥤🥤🥤🥤🥤🥤🥤

Post Picture ☐

Exercise	Exercise

Book .... Pages ....

notes:

NOW

Date: Day: **NOW** ♠

Diet

Breakfast

Lunch

Dinner

Water 🥛🥛🥛🥛🥛🥛🥛🥛

Post Picture ☐

Exercise	Exercise

Book ....   Pages ....

notes:

NOW

Date: Day: NOW ♠

Diet

Breakfast

Lunch

Dinner

Water ⊔⊔⊔⊔⊔⊔⊔⊔

Post Picture ☐

Exercise	Exercise

Book .... Pages ....

notes:

NOW ♠

Date: Day: **NOW** ♠

Diet

Breakfast

Lunch

Dinner

Water ⊔⊔⊔⊔⊔⊔⊔⊔

Post Picture ☐

Exercise	Exercise

Book .... Pages ....

notes:

NOW ♠

Date: Day: NOW ♠

Diet

Breakfast

Lunch

Dinner

Water ▽▽▽▽▽▽▽▽

Post Picture ☐

Exercise   ⋮ Exercise

Book .... Pages ....

notes:

Date: Day:

NOW ♠

Diet

Breakfast

Lunch

Dinner

Water 🥛🥛🥛🥛🥛🥛🥛🥛

Post Picture ☐

Exercise | Exercise

Book

Pages

notes:

NOW

Date: Day: **NOW**

Diet

Breakfast
....

Lunch
....

Dinner
....

Water 🥛🥛🥛🥛🥛🥛🥛🥛

Post Picture ☐

Exercise	Exercise

Book .... Pages ....

notes:

NOW ♠

Date: Day: NOW ♠

Diet

Breakfast

Lunch

Dinner

Water ⛉⛉⛉⛉⛉⛉⛉⛉

Post Picture ☐

Exercise	Exercise

Book   Pages

notes:

NOW ♠

Date: Day: **NOW** ♠

Diet

Breakfast

Lunch

Dinner

Water ⊔⊔⊔⊔⊔⊔⊔⊔

Post Picture ☐

Exercise	Exercise

Book .... Pages ....

notes:

NOW ♠

Date: Day: **NOW** ♠

Diet

Breakfast

Lunch

Dinner

Water ⊔⊔⊔⊔⊔⊔⊔⊔

Post Picture ☐

Exercise	Exercise

Book .... Pages ....

notes:

NOW

PHASE 1

rt Date .... Start Weight ....
d Date .... Goal Weight ....

◯ ◯ ◯ ◯ ◯ ◯ ◯ ◯ ◯ ◯

◯ ◯ ◯ ◯ ◯ ◯ ◯ ◯ ◯ ◯

◯ ◯ ◯ ◯ ◯ (30)

Finish first seventy-five days. Then, either take a break for no more than 30 days, and start Phase 1.

In addition to rules of first seventy five days, you must:

 complete three critical tasks each day

 do 10 minutes of visualization

 take a 5-minute COLD shower

notes:

NOW

Date: dd / mm / yyyy   Day: /

Diet

Breakfast *3 eggs, 4 bacon, toast*
almonds

Lunch
avocado salad with 1000 islands dressing
protein shake with blueberries

Dinner *beef and bean chili*
3 carrots

Water *8 sixteen oz pints of water*

Visualization
earning
the
promotion

Post Picture Cold Shower

Exercise

6am, 20 mins cardio
stretch
3 sets, 20 squats

4 sets, 80lb calf raise
2 sets, 100lb deadlift

Exercise

10 mins core
8pm, 20 mins cardio

3 sets, 20lb curls
3 sets, 30lb flys
4 sets, 20lb trys

Task 1
pay insurance

Task 2
celebrate
anniversary

Task 3
story time with
my daughter

Book *The Shift, W. Dyer* Pages *23-35*

notes:

NOW

Date: Day: **PHASE 1** ♠

Diet

Breakfast

Lunch

Dinner

Visualization

Water

Post Picture ☐ Cold Shower ☐

Exercise	Exercise

Task 1   Task 2   Task 3

Book   Pages

notes:

NOW

Date: _____ Day: _____ **PHASE 1** ♠

Diet

Breakfast

Visualization

Lunch

Dinner

Water ▽▽▽▽▽▽▽▽

Post Picture ☐ Cold Shower ☐

Exercise

Exercise

Task 1

Task 2

Task 3

Book _____ Pages _____

notes:

NOW ♠

Date: _____ Day: _____ **PHASE 1** ♠

Diet

Breakfast

Visualization

Lunch

Dinner

Water 🥤🥤🥤🥤🥤🥤🥤🥤

Post Picture ☐ Cold Shower ☐

Exercise | Exercise

Task 1 | Task 2 | Task 3

Book _____ Pages _____

notes:

NOW

Date: _____   Day: _____   **PHASE 1** ♠

Diet

Breakfast

Visualization

Lunch

Dinner

Water 🥛🥛🥛🥛🥛🥛🥛🥛

Post Picture ☐ Cold Shower ☐

Exercise

Exercise

Task 1   Task 2   Task 3

Book _____   Pages _____

notes:

NOW ♠

Date: _____   Day: _____

Diet

Breakfast

Lunch

Dinner

Visualization

Water 🥤🥤🥤🥤🥤🥤🥤🥤

Post Picture ☐ Cold Shower ☐

Exercise	Exercise

Task 1   Task 2   Task 3

Book _____   Pages _____

notes:

NOW ♠

Date: _____   Day: _____

Diet

Breakfast

Lunch

Dinner

Visualization

Water 🥤🥤🥤🥤🥤🥤🥤🥤

Post Picture ☐ Cold Shower ☐

Exercise

Exercise

Task 1

Task 2

Task 3

Book _____   Pages _____

notes:

NOW ♠

Date: Day: **PHASE 1** ♠

Diet

Breakfast

Visualization

Lunch

Dinner

Water 🥛🥛🥛🥛🥛🥛🥛🥛

Post Picture ☐ Cold Shower ☐

Exercise : Exercise

Task 1 : Task 2 : Task 3

Book .... Pages ....

notes:

NOW ♠

Date: Day: **PHASE 1**

Diet

Breakfast Visualization

Lunch

Dinner

Water

Post Picture ☐ Cold Shower ☐

Exercise | Exercise

Task 1 | Task 2 | Task 3

Book Pages

notes:

NOW

Date: _____ Day: _____ **PHASE 1** ♠

Diet

Breakfast

Lunch

Dinner

Visualization

Water ⛆⛆⛆⛆⛆⛆⛆⛆

Post Picture ☐ Cold Shower ☐

Exercise	Exercise

Task 1   Task 2   Task 3

Book _____ Pages _____

notes:

Date: Day: **PHASE 1** ♠

Diet

Breakfast Visualization

Lunch

Dinner

Water 🥤🥤🥤🥤🥤🥤🥤🥤

Post Picture ☐ Cold Shower ☐

Exercise Exercise

Task 1 Task 2 Task 3

Book .... Pages ....

notes:

NOW ♠

Date: _____   Day: _____   **PHASE 1** ♠

Diet

Breakfast

Visualization

Lunch

Dinner

Water ⊔ ⊔ ⊔ ⊔ ⊔ ⊔ ⊔ ⊔

Post Picture ☐ Cold Shower ☐

Exercise

Exercise

Task 1

Task 2

Task 3

Book _____ Pages _____

notes:

NOW ♠

Date: _____ Day: _____

Diet

Breakfast

Lunch

Dinner

Visualization

Water 🥤🥤🥤🥤🥤🥤🥤🥤

Post Picture ☐ Cold Shower ☐

Exercise

Exercise

Task 1

Task 2

Task 3

Book .... Pages ....

notes:

NOW ♠

Date: Day: **PHASE 1** ♠

Diet

Breakfast

Visualization

Lunch

Dinner

Water ⊔ ⊔ ⊔ ⊔ ⊔ ⊔ ⊔ ⊔

Post Picture ☐ Cold Shower ☐

Exercise | Exercise

Task 1 | Task 2 | Task 3

Book .... Pages ....

notes:

NOW ♠

Date: Day: **PHASE 1** ♠

Diet

Breakfast

Visualization

Lunch

Dinner

Water 🥤🥤🥤🥤🥤🥤🥤🥤

Post Picture ☐ Cold Shower ☐

Exercise | Exercise

Task 1 | Task 2 | Task 3

Book .... Pages ....

notes:

NOW ♠

Date: Day: **PHASE 1** ♠

Diet

Breakfast

Visualization

Lunch

Dinner

Water 🥤🥤🥤🥤🥤🥤🥤🥤

Post Picture ☐ Cold Shower ☐

Exercise : Exercise

Task 1 : Task 2 : Task 3

Book _____ Pages _____

notes:

NOW ♠

Date: _____ Day: _____ **PHASE 1** ♠

Diet

Breakfast

Visualization

Lunch

Dinner

Water 🥤🥤🥤🥤🥤🥤🥤🥤

Post Picture ☐ Cold Shower ☐

Exercise	Exercise

Task 1   Task 2   Task 3

Book .... Pages ....

notes:

NOW ♠

Date: Day: **PHASE 1**

Diet

Breakfast

Visualization

Lunch

Dinner

Water 🥛🥛🥛🥛🥛🥛🥛🥛

Post Picture ☐ Cold Shower ☐

Exercise

Exercise

Task 1　Task 2　Task 3

Book

Pages

notes:

NOW

Date: Day: **PHASE 1** ♠

Diet

Breakfast   Visualization

Lunch

Dinner

Water

Post Picture ☐ Cold Shower ☐

Exercise	Exercise

Task 1	Task 2	Task 3

Book   Pages

notes:

NOW ♠

Date: Day: **PHASE 1**

Diet

Breakfast

Visualization

Lunch

Dinner

Water 🥤🥤🥤🥤🥤🥤🥤🥤

Post Picture ☐ Cold Shower ☐

Exercise | Exercise

Task 1 | Task 2 | Task 3

Book .... Pages ....

notes:

NOW

Date: Day: **PHASE 1**

Diet

Breakfast

Visualization

Lunch

Dinner

Water

Post Picture ☐ Cold Shower ☐

Exercise | Exercise

Task 1 | Task 2 | Task 3

Book Pages

notes:

NOW ♠

Date: _____   Day: _____

Diet

Breakfast

Visualization

Lunch

Dinner

Water ⊔ ⊔ ⊔ ⊔ ⊔ ⊔ ⊔ ⊔

Post Picture ☐ Cold Shower ☐

Exercise | Exercise

Task 1   Task 2   Task 3

Book _____   Pages _____

notes:

NOW ♠

Date: Day: **PHASE 1** ♠

Diet

Breakfast   Visualization

Lunch

Dinner

Water

Post Picture ☐ Cold Shower ☐

| Exercise | Exercise |

Task 1   Task 2   Task 3

Book   Pages

notes:

NOW ♠

Date: _____   Day: _____   **PHASE 1** ♠

Diet

Breakfast .... Visualization

Lunch

Dinner

Water 🥤🥤🥤🥤🥤🥤🥤🥤

Post Picture ☐ Cold Shower ☐

Exercise : Exercise

Task 1 : Task 2 : Task 3

Book .... Pages ....

notes:

NOW

Date: _____   Day: _____   **PHASE 1** ♠

Diet

Breakfast	Visualization
Lunch	
Dinner	

Water 🥛🥛🥛🥛🥛🥛🥛🥛

Post Picture ☐ Cold Shower ☐

| Exercise | Exercise |

| Task 1 | Task 2 | Task 3 |

Book .... Pages ....

notes:

Date: Day: **PHASE 1** ♠

Diet

Breakfast Visualization

Lunch

Dinner

Water 🥤🥤🥤🥤🥤🥤🥤🥤

Post Picture ☐ Cold Shower ☐

Exercise | Exercise

Task 1 | Task 2 | Task 3

Book .... Pages ....

notes:

Date: Day: **PHASE 1**

Diet

Breakfast

Visualization

Lunch

Dinner

Water

Post Picture ☐ Cold Shower ☐

Exercise : Exercise

Task 1 : Task 2 : Task 3

Book .... Pages ....

notes:

NOW

Date: Day: **PHASE 1** ♠

Diet

Breakfast

Visualization

Lunch

Dinner

Water

Post Picture ☐ Cold Shower ☐

Exercise

Exercise

Task 1   Task 2   Task 3

Book   Pages

notes:

Date: _____ Day: _____ **PHASE 1** ♠

Diet

Breakfast .... Visualization

Lunch

Dinner

Water 🥛🥛🥛🥛🥛🥛🥛🥛

Post Picture ☐ Cold Shower ☐

Exercise | Exercise

Task 1 | Task 2 | Task 3

Book _____ Pages _____

notes:

NOW ♠

Date: _____ Day: _____ **PHASE 1** ♠

Diet

Breakfast

Lunch

Dinner

Visualization

Water ⊔⊔⊔⊔⊔⊔⊔⊔

Post Picture ☐ Cold Shower ☐

Exercise

Exercise

Task 1

Task 2

Task 3

Book _____ Pages _____

notes:

Date: Day: **PHASE 1**

Diet

Breakfast

Visualization

Lunch

Dinner

Water

Post Picture ☐ Cold Shower ☐

Exercise | Exercise

Task 1 | Task 2 | Task 3

Book .... Pages ....

notes:

NOW

PHASE 2

rt Date .... Start Weight ....

d Date .... Goal Weight ....

○ ○ ○ ○ ○ ○ ○ ○ ○ ○

○ ○ ○ ○ ○ ○ ○ ○ ○ ○

○ ○ ○ ○ ○ (30)

You must wait 30 days after completing phase 1

There are NO additional tasks for phase two.

Repeat the same rules from 75 DAY Challenge.

notes:

NOW

Date: .... Day: ....

Diet

Breakfast

Lunch

Dinner

Water ⊔ ⊔ ⊔ ⊔ ⊔ ⊔ ⊔ ⊔

Post Picture ☐

Exercise	Exercise

Book .... Pages ....

notes:

NOW

Date: Day: **PHASE 2**

Diet

Breakfast

Lunch

Dinner

Water

Post Picture ☐

Exercise	Exercise

Book Pages

notes:

NOW ♠

Date: Day: **PHASE 2**

Diet

Breakfast

Lunch

Dinner

Water

Post Picture ☐

Exercise	Exercise

Book   Pages

notes:

NOW

Date: Day: **PHASE 2** ♠

Diet

Breakfast

Lunch

Dinner

Water 🥛🥛🥛🥛🥛🥛🥛🥛

Post Picture ☐

Exercise	Exercise

Book Pages

notes:

NOW ♠

Date: Day: **PHASE 2** ♠

Diet

Breakfast

....

Lunch

....

Dinner

....

Water ▽▽▽▽▽▽▽▽

Post Picture ☐

Exercise	Exercise

Book .... Pages ....

notes:

NOW ♠

Date: Day:

Diet

Breakfast

Lunch

Dinner

Water ▽▽▽▽▽▽▽▽

Post Picture ☐

Exercise	Exercise

Book .... Pages ....

notes:

NOW

Date: Day:

Diet

Breakfast

Lunch

Dinner

Water ⛃⛃⛃⛃⛃⛃⛃⛃

Post Picture ☐

Exercise	Exercise

Book ....   Pages ....

notes:

NOW ♠

Date: Day: **PHASE 2**

Diet

Breakfast

Lunch

Dinner

Water

Post Picture ☐

Exercise	Exercise

Book .... Pages ....

notes:

NOW ♠

Date: Day: **PHASE 2** ♠

Diet

Breakfast

Lunch

Dinner

Water

Post Picture ☐

Exercise	Exercise

Book   Pages

notes:

NOW ♠

Date: Day: **PHASE 2** ♠

Diet

Breakfast

Lunch

Dinner

Water 🥛🥛🥛🥛🥛🥛🥛🥛

Post Picture ☐

Exercise	Exercise

Book .... Pages ....

notes:

NOW

Date: Day: **PHASE 2**

Diet

Breakfast

Lunch

Dinner

Water ▽▽▽▽▽▽▽▽

Post Picture ☐

Exercise	Exercise

Book

Pages

notes:

NOW

Date: _____ Day: _____ **PHASE 2** ♠

Diet

Breakfast

Lunch

Dinner

Water ⊔⊔⊔⊔⊔⊔⊔⊔

Post Picture ☐

Exercise	Exercise

Book .... Pages ....

notes:

NOW

Date: Day: **PHASE 2**

Diet

Breakfast

Lunch

Dinner

Water

Post Picture ☐

Exercise | Exercise

Book   Pages

notes:

NOW ♠

Date: _____ Day: _____

Diet

....
Breakfast

....
Lunch

....
Dinner

....
Water ⊔⊔⊔⊔⊔⊔⊔⊔

Post Picture ☐

Exercise	Exercise

Book .... Pages ....

notes:

NOW ♠

Date: Day: **PHASE 2** ♠

Diet

Breakfast

....

Lunch

....

Dinner

....

Water ⊔⊔⊔⊔⊔⊔⊔⊔

Post Picture ☐

Exercise : Exercise

Book .... Pages ....

notes:

NOW ♠

Date: Day: **PHASE 2**

Diet

Breakfast

Lunch

Dinner

Water ⊔⊔⊔⊔⊔⊔⊔⊔

Post Picture ☐

Exercise	Exercise

Book .... Pages ....

notes:

NOW

Date: Day: **PHASE 2** ♠

Diet

Breakfast

Lunch

Dinner

Water ⊔⊔⊔⊔⊔⊔⊔⊔

Post Picture ☐

Exercise | Exercise

Book .... Pages ....

notes:

NOW ♠

Date: Day: **PHASE 2** ♠

Diet

Breakfast

Lunch

Dinner

Water ⊔ ⊔ ⊔ ⊔ ⊔ ⊔ ⊔ ⊔

Post Picture ☐

Exercise   Exercise

Book .... Pages ....

notes:

NOW

Date: Day: **PHASE 2**

Diet

Breakfast

Lunch

Dinner

Water

Post Picture ☐

Exercise	Exercise

Book .... Pages ....

notes:

NOW

Date: Day: **PHASE 2** ♠

Diet

Breakfast

Lunch

Dinner

Water 🥤🥤🥤🥤🥤🥤🥤🥤

Post Picture ☐

Exercise	Exercise

Book .... Pages ....

notes:

NOW

Date: Day: **PHASE 2**

Diet
Breakfast

Lunch

Dinner

Water

Post Picture ☐

Exercise	Exercise

Book

Pages

notes:

NOW

Date: Day: **PHASE 2**

Diet

Breakfast

Lunch

Dinner

Water ⊔⊔⊔⊔⊔⊔⊔⊔

Post Picture ☐

Exercise	Exercise

Book .... Pages ....

notes:

NOW ♠

Date: Day: **PHASE 2**

Diet

Breakfast

Lunch

Dinner

Water

Post Picture ☐

Exercise	Exercise

Book   Pages

notes:

NOW ♠

Date: Day: **PHASE 2** ♠

Diet

Breakfast

Lunch

Dinner

Water ▽▽▽▽▽▽▽▽

Post Picture ☐

Exercise ⋮ Exercise

Book

Pages

notes:

NOW

Date: Day: **PHASE 2** ♠

Diet

Breakfast

Lunch

Dinner

Water ⛉⛉⛉⛉⛉⛉⛉⛉

Post Picture ☐

Exercise   Exercise

Book .... Pages ....

notes:

NOW

Date: Day: **PHASE 2** ♠

Diet

Breakfast
....

Lunch
....

Dinner
....

Water ▽▽▽▽▽▽▽▽
....

Post Picture ☐

Exercise	Exercise

Book .... Pages ....

notes:

NOW

Date: Day:

Diet

Breakfast

Lunch

Dinner

Water

Post Picture ☐

Exercise	Exercise

Book   Pages

notes:

NOW

Date: _____ Day: _____ **PHASE 2** ♠

Diet

....
Breakfast

....
Lunch

....
Dinner

....
Water 🥛🥛🥛🥛🥛🥛🥛🥛
....

Post Picture ☐

Exercise	Exercise

Book .... Pages ....

notes:

NOW ♠

Date: Day: **PHASE 2** ♠

Diet

Breakfast

Lunch

Dinner

Water ⊔ ⊔ ⊔ ⊔ ⊔ ⊔ ⊔ ⊔

Post Picture ☐

Exercise	Exercise

Book .... Pages ....

notes:

NOW ♠

Date: Day: **PHASE 2** ♠

Diet

Breakfast

Lunch

Dinner

Water 🥤🥤🥤🥤🥤🥤🥤🥤

Post Picture ☐

Exercise	Exercise

Book .... Pages ....

notes:

NOW

PHASE 3

rt Date .... Start Weight ....

d Date .... Goal Weight ....

○○○○○○○○○○○

○○○○○○○○○○○

○○○○○ (30)

Start this phase exactly 30 days before 1-year anniversary of first 75 day challenge.

In addition to rules of first seventy five days, you must:

 complete three critical tasks each day

do 10 minutes of visualization

 take a 5-minute COLD shower

talk to a stranger

 do a random act of kindness

notes:

NOW ♠

Date: Day: **PHASE 3** ♠

Diet

Breakfast

Visualization

Lunch

Dinner

Water 🥛🥛🥛🥛🥛🥛🥛🥛

Post Picture ☐ Cold Shower ☐

Exercise | Exercise

Stranger ☐ | Kindness ☐

Task 1 | Task 2 | Task 3

Book .... Pages ....

notes:

NOW ♠

Date: Day: **PHASE 3**

Diet

Breakfast

Visualization

Lunch

Dinner

Water

Post Picture ☐ Cold Shower ☐

Exercise | Exercise

Stranger ☐ | Kindness ☐

Task 1 | Task 2 | Task 3

Book .... Pages ....

notes:

NOW

Date: Day: **PHASE 3**

Diet

Breakfast

Visualization

Lunch

Dinner

Water

Post Picture ☐ Cold Shower ☐

Exercise

Exercise

Stranger ☐   Kindness ☐

Task 1   Task 2   Task 3

Book   Pages

notes:

NOW

Date: Day: **PHASE 3** ♠

Diet

Breakfast   Visualization

Lunch

Dinner

Water ᗊᗊᗊᗊᗊᗊᗊᗊ

Post Picture ☐ Cold Shower ☐

Exercise   Exercise

Stranger ☐   Kindness ☐

Task 1   Task 2   Task 3

Book   Pages

notes:

Date: Day: **PHASE 3**

Diet

Breakfast | Visualization

Lunch

Dinner

Water 🥤🥤🥤🥤🥤🥤🥤🥤

Post Picture ☐ Cold Shower ☐

Exercise | Exercise

Stranger ☐ | Kindness ☐

Task 1 | Task 2 | Task 3

Book .... Pages ....

notes:

Date: _____ Day: _____ **♠ PHASE 3**

Diet

Breakfast .... Visualization

Lunch

Dinner

Water 🥛🥛🥛🥛🥛🥛🥛🥛

Post Picture ☐ Cold Shower ☐

Exercise	Exercise
Stranger ☐	Kindness ☐

Task 1 .... Task 2 .... Task 3

Book .... Pages ....

notes:

NOW

Date: Day: **PHASE 3**

Diet

Breakfast

Visualization

Lunch

Dinner

Water

Post Picture ☐ Cold Shower ☐

Exercise | Exercise

Stranger ☐ | Kindness ☐

Task 1 | Task 2 | Task 3

Book

Pages

notes:

NOW

Date: Day: **PHASE 3**

Diet

Breakfast

Lunch

Dinner

Visualization

Water ∪∪∪∪∪∪∪∪

Post Picture ☐ Cold Shower ☐

Exercise

Exercise

Stranger ☐

Kindness ☐

Task 1

Task 2

Task 3

Book

Pages

notes:

NOW

Date: Day: **PHASE 3**

Diet

Breakfast

Visualization

Lunch

Dinner

Water

Post Picture ☐ Cold Shower ☐

Exercise

Exercise

Stranger ☐   Kindness ☐

Task 1   Task 2   Task 3

Book   Pages

notes:

NOW ♠

Date: Day:

PHASE 3

Diet

Breakfast   Visualization

Lunch

Dinner

Water 🥤🥤🥤🥤🥤🥤🥤🥤

Post Picture ☐ Cold Shower ☐

Exercise   Exercise

Stranger ☐   Kindness ☐

Task 1   Task 2   Task 3

Book   Pages

notes:

NOW ♠

Date: Day: **PHASE 3**

Diet

Breakfast

Visualization

Lunch

Dinner

Water

Post Picture ☐ Cold Shower ☐

Exercise | Exercise

Stranger ☐ | Kindness ☐

Task 1 | Task 2 | Task 3

Book | Pages

notes:

NOW

Date: _____ Day: _____ **PHASE 3** ♠

Diet

Breakfast

Lunch

Dinner

Visualization

Water ▽▽▽▽▽▽▽▽

Post Picture ☐ Cold Shower ☐

Exercise

Exercise

Stranger ☐

Kindness ☐

Task 1

Task 2

Task 3

Book .... Pages ....

notes:

NOW

Date: Day: **PHASE 3** ♠

Diet

Breakfast | Visualization

Lunch

Dinner

Water ▽▽▽▽▽▽▽▽

Post Picture ☐ Cold Shower ☐

Exercise | Exercise

Stranger ☐ | Kindness ☐

Task 1 | Task 2 | Task 3

Book .... Pages ....

notes:

NOW

Date: Day: **PHASE 3**

Diet

Breakfast · Visualization

Lunch

Dinner

Water

Post Picture ☐ Cold Shower☐

Exercise ┊Exercise

Stranger ☐ ┊ Kindness ☐

Task 1 ┊ Task 2 ┊ Task 3

Book Pages

notes:

Date: Day: **PHASE 3**

Diet

Breakfast | Visualization

Lunch

Dinner

Water 🥛🥛🥛🥛🥛🥛🥛🥛

Post Picture ☐ Cold Shower ☐

Exercise | Exercise

Stranger ☐ | Kindness ☐

Task 1 | Task 2 | Task 3

Book .... Pages ....

notes:

NOW

Date: Day: **PHASE 3**

Diet

Breakfast   Visualization

Lunch

Dinner

Water

Post Picture ☐ Cold Shower ☐

Exercise   Exercise

Stranger ☐   Kindness ☐

Task 1   Task 2   Task 3

Book   Pages

notes:

NOW ♠

Date: Day: **PHASE 3** ♠

Diet

Breakfast .... Visualization

Lunch

Dinner

Water 🥤🥤🥤🥤🥤🥤🥤🥤

Post Picture ☐ Cold Shower ☐

Exercise | Exercise

Stranger ☐ | Kindness ☐

Task 1 | Task 2 | Task 3

Book .... Pages ....

notes:

NOW

Date: Day: **PHASE 3**

Diet

Breakfast

Visualization

Lunch

Dinner

Water

Post Picture ☐ Cold Shower ☐

Exercise

Exercise

Stranger ☐

Kindness ☐

Task 1

Task 2

Task 3

Book

Pages

notes:

NOW

Date: Day: **PHASE 3**

Diet

Breakfast

Visualization

Lunch

Dinner

Water 🥤🥤🥤🥤🥤🥤🥤🥤

Post Picture ☐ Cold Shower ☐

Exercise

Exercise

Stranger ☐

Kindness ☐

Task 1 Task 2 Task 3

Book .... Pages ....

notes:

NOW ♠

Date: Day: **PHASE 3**

Diet

Breakfast Visualization

Lunch

Dinner

Water

Post Picture ☐ Cold Shower☐

Exercise | Exercise

Stranger ☐ | Kindness ☐

Task 1 | Task 2 | Task 3

Book

Pages

notes:

NOW

Date: Day: **PHASE 3**

Diet

Breakfast .... Visualization

Lunch

Dinner

Water

Post Picture ☐ Cold Shower ☐

Exercise | Exercise

Stranger ☐ | Kindness ☐

Task 1 | Task 2 | Task 3

Book .... Pages ....

notes:

Date: Day: **PHASE 3** ♠

Diet

Breakfast   Visualization

Lunch

Dinner

Water

Post Picture ☐ Cold Shower ☐

Exercise   Exercise

Stranger ☐   Kindness ☐

Task 1   Task 2   Task 3

Book   Pages

notes:

NOW ♠

Date: Day: **PHASE 3**

Diet

Breakfast

Lunch

Dinner

Visualization

Water

Post Picture ☐ Cold Shower ☐

Exercise | Exercise

Stranger ☐ | Kindness ☐

Task 1 | Task 2 | Task 3

Book

Pages

notes:

NOW ♠

Date: Day: **PHASE 3** ♠

Diet

Breakfast   Visualization

Lunch

Dinner

Water ⊔⊔⊔⊔⊔⊔⊔⊔

Post Picture ☐ Cold Shower ☐

Exercise   Exercise

Stranger ☐   Kindness ☐

Task 1   Task 2   Task 3

Book   Pages

notes:

NOW

Date: Day: **PHASE 3**

Diet

Breakfast

Lunch

Dinner

Visualization

Water

Post Picture ☐ Cold Shower ☐

Exercise

Exercise

Stranger ☐

Kindness ☐

Task 1

Task 2

Task 3

Book

Pages

notes:

NOW ♠

Date: _____   Day: _____   **PHASE 3** ♠

Diet

Breakfast .... Visualization

Lunch

Dinner

Water 🥤🥤🥤🥤🥤🥤🥤🥤

Post Picture ☐ Cold Shower ☐

Exercise   ## Exercise

Stranger ☐   Kindness ☐

Task 1   Task 2   Task 3

Book .... Pages ....

notes:

NOW ♠

Date: _____ Day: _____ **PHASE 3** ♠

Diet

Breakfast

Lunch

Dinner

Visualization

Water ⊔⊔⊔⊔⊔⊔⊔⊔

Post Picture ☐ Cold Shower ☐

Exercise

Exercise

Stranger ☐

Kindness ☐

Task 1 _____ Task 2 _____ Task 3 _____

Book _____ Pages _____

notes:

NOW ♠

Date: Day: **PHASE 3** ♠

Diet

Breakfast   Visualization

Lunch

Dinner

Water

Post Picture ☐ Cold Shower ☐

Exercise   Exercise

Stranger ☐   Kindness ☐

Task 1   Task 2   Task 3

Book   Pages

notes:

NOW ♠

Date: Day: **PHASE 3** ♠

Diet

Breakfast

Visualization

Lunch

Dinner

Water

Post Picture ☐ Cold Shower ☐

Exercise

Exercise

Stranger ☐

Kindness ☐

Task 1

Task 2

Task 3

Book

Pages

notes:

NOW

Date: Day: **PHASE 1**

Diet

Breakfast

Visualization

Lunch

Dinner

Water

Post Picture ☐ Cold Shower ☐

Exercise | Exercise

Task 1 | Task 2 | Task 3

Book .... Pages ....

Printed in the USA
CPSIA information can be obtained
at www.ICGtesting.com
CBHW050530270724
12290CB00011B/459